GOD HELP ME UNDERSTAND

by Dorothy LaCroix Hill

illustrated by William A. McCaffery

Abingdon Press

New York   *Nashville*

To the many boys and girls
whose questions have forced
me to examine thoughtfully
my own Christian faith.

Contents

I Wonder about God

How could God always be?

Is God greater than men yet know?

How can I know that there is a God?

How am I created in the image of God?

without beginning and without end

Wheels began to go around in Ben's head as Mr. Perkins said, "Here is an idea about God that stretches your mind!"

With a kind of wonder in his voice Mr. Perkins read,

> "The God of Abraham praise,
> All praised be His Name,
> Who was, and is, and is to be,
> And still the same!

The one eternal God,
Ere aught that now appears;
The First, the Last: beyond all thought
His timeless years!"

"The God of Abraham" made Ben think back a long way. Abraham lived three thousand years ago. And long before that there was God. Before there was anything on the earth, there was God. God always was, and always would be!

Mr. Perkins was right. The idea did stretch Ben's mind. In fact, his mind just would not stretch that far. Everything he had ever heard about had a beginning and would probably have an end. As he glanced around his sixth-grade Sunday school class, he decided that no one else could stretch his mind that far either. Everyone in the class looked puzzled.

In church Ben looked up the hymn again. During most of the sermon he puzzled about it. How could there be "timeless years?" he wondered. A year was 365 days. Could there be years that were not measured by days, or months, or any kind of time?

"It certainly is 'beyond all thought,'" Ben said to himself. "That part of the hymn is true. The whole thing is just too big to think about." He put the hymnal back in the rack and forgot about it.

Then, months later, during a family vacation trip, he remembered.

In the darkness of early morning the family sat around the breakfast fire outside their tent. Far to the east the sun was rising, and to the west the first rosy light played against the faces of the mountains.

Mother spoke softly and slowly, with the same kind of wonder in her voice that had been in Mr. Perkins'.

"Lord, thou hast been our dwelling place
    in all generations.
Before the mountains were brought forth,
    or ever thou hadst formed the earth and the
        world,
        from everlasting to everlasting thou art God." *

"God is older than the mountains," Ben reflected.

"God can't be old," Mother answered thoughtfully, "or young, either. Age and time are only for human beings."

"I can't seem to understand that," Ben said. "When I try to think about it, the whole idea sort of slips away. It's too much for me."

"Too much for all of us," Father agreed. "But we can't expect to understand everything about God."

"Everlasting," Ben murmured. "The mountains look like that—as if they always have been and always will be. They help me get the idea a little— from everlasting to everlasting thou art God."

* Psalm 90:1-2

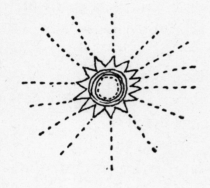

an atom and a universe

"Guess what!" Jill shouted as she rushed breathlessly into the house. "Tomorrow our class is going to the high school to see the Science Fair."

"Fine," said Mrs. West. "Bill has just been telling me about it."

"Huh!" grunted Jill's high-school brother. "Why should they bring you kids to the fair? You won't know what it's all about. Roger has a swell model of the solar system. And Russ has an exhibit about the atom. But you won't understand them."

"That's not true, is it, Mother?" cried Jill. "We have science in school, and it's not so hard. I'll understand plenty of things at the fair, Mr. Know-It-All Bill West!"

"Well, go if you have to." Bill shrugged his shoulders. "But when you get home tomorrow you won't know any more than you do right now. In fact, I'll buy you a strawberry soda if you can explain even one new thing you've learned!"

"Fine!" Jill nodded confidently. "You've got a date at the drugstore tomorrow after school."

Jill's class spent the next afternoon at the fair.

"Look at the exhibits you are most interested in," Miss Merryford said, "but watch the clock above this door. We'll meet right here at exactly three o'clock. Our bus will be waiting."

Jill looked first for Roger's model of the solar system. The sun was a plastic ball filled with something that made it blindingly bright. Around the sun, each in its own orbit, were the planets: Mercury, Venus, Earth, Mars, Jupiter, Saturn, Uranus, Neptune, and Pluto. Roger was there to explain the exhibit.

"Earth travels all the way around the sun in one year—365 days," Roger said. "But Pluto way out here needs 248 of our years to make just one trip. Being so far from the sun means that Pluto is probably wearing a thick jacket of ice. Uranus and Neptune are probably covered with ice, too."

12

"Where are the stars?" Jill asked. She was eager to get as much information from Roger as possible. Bill would see that she could understand things like the universe!

"Way out beyond all this!" Roger waved his hand toward the ceiling and toward the ends of the big room. "There are millions and millions of stars, each one fiery hot and giving off intense light like our sun. But they are all so far away that the light we see is just a tiny point in the sky. Why, the nearest star, Alpha, in the constellation Centaur, is twenty-six trillion miles from our solar system."

Constellation, trillion, solar system. The words buzzed around in Jill's head.

"And some of the other stars may have planets revolving around them just like our sun does," Roger went on. "Maybe people live on some of them."

Jill let out a long breath. "Whee-ee-ee-oo. That sounds too big for me."

Roger laughed. "If this is too big, try Russ' exhibit about the atom. Maybe that's more your size. Russ says that one hundred million atoms laid end to end would be only an inch long!"

Jill sighed. The atom exhibit sounded hard, too. But maybe when she saw it, she would understand it.

The exhibit was mostly charts. Russ was standing near by, ready to explain them.

"What does all this mean?" Jill asked.

"It means that everything you think is solid isn't really solid at all," Russ said. "Everything is made up of jillions and jillions of atoms. And the inside of an atom is mostly empty space."

"It can't be all empty space," said Jill. "There must be something there."

"Oh, there is," laughed Russ. "Look here," he said, pointing to a chart. "Inside each atom are protons, neutrons, and electrons. The protons and neutrons are these blue and red beads inside this tiny center that we call the nucleus."

"Nucleus," said Jill, trying to become accustomed to another strange word so that she would remember it. "How big is the nucleus? Roger says that atoms are small to begin with."

"The nucleus is only one million-billionth of the atom's total size," Russ said. "It's small, but it's crowded with neutrons and protons."

Jill shook her head. "I can't imagine anything so huge as the universe, and I can't imagine anything so small as the atom. But what about these things floating around the nucleus? What are they?"

"These yellow beads are electrons," said Russ. "They whirl around the nucleus just as the planets whirl around the sun."

"You mean all that is happening in something too tiny even to see?" Jill asked wonderingly.

"All that and a lot more!" Russ said. "Wait a

minute. I haven't told you how the atom splits and releases atomic energy."

"Don't say any more!" Jill cried. "I'm all mixed up about what you've told me already. It would take me at least a year to understand about atoms. Why did I ever tell Bill it would be easy to understand things here at the fair?"

She moved on to the next exhibit, which was WONDERS OF THE ATOMIC AGE. She looked at pictures of atomic-powered submarines and atomic-powered aircraft. She studied the sketch of a small reactor that could provide power from split uranium atoms to heat a whole city. A poster said that some day electrical power would be so plentiful and so cheap that all people could afford to use as much as they wanted.

Jill just stared at the exhibit. There was nothing here that could really be explained to Bill. She was about to forget the strawberry soda when she caught sight of the next exhibit. Her face brightened.

"Well, hello," she murmured. "At least I know something about you!"

It was a model of a human being. Jill opened the hinged door that was the rib cage and looked in at the lungs and heart. It was much more complicated than she had thought it would be.

Miss Merryford stood near by watching Jill's astonished face.

"God did something wonderful when he made you, didn't he?" she asked.

"I'll say!" Jill answered. "He did lots of things I never knew about before."

The rest of the afternoon went quickly. When the clock said three, Jill still had not found anything she could actually explain to Bill.

"Well, what did you learn?" he asked the moment she got home. "Was it worth going?"

"You were right. It was hard to understand," Jill admitted. "I guess I really can't explain anything I saw. But I did learn that God created a wonderful universe and that it will take a long, long time before anyone understands all the things that happen in it."

"That was a good discovery," laughed Mrs. West. "Some people never find out how little they know."

Bill grinned. "I found out," he said. "The fair was fun, and I learned a lot. But the biggest thing I learned was that I didn't know very much. When do you want that strawberry soda?"

"Right now," said Jill. "I'm ready for it."

be still and know that I am God

The summer Sam was eleven, his family rented a cottage on one of the Great Lakes. He and his mother and his five-year-old brother, Davey, spent the whole summer there. On Friday evenings Sam's father came from the city for the week end.

At first Sam enjoyed the long, lazy weeks at the beach. He played with Davey and swam with boys from cottages near by. But after a while the days grew a little tiresome. Something was missing, and he couldn't quite put his finger on what it was. The week ends with his father were better, but there was still something Sam wanted and couldn't seem to find.

Each evening, after an early supper, the family went down to the shore until bedtime. Sam swam and played with the other boys, or helped Davey build sand castles. When the lake was quiet, he and Davey sometimes tried to skip flat stones across the water, or hunted for shells that the waves had carried up to the beach. There were so many things to do that the boys were seldom quiet.

Then one evening when Davy had trotted off to get some water in a big shell, Sam dropped down on the sand beside his mother. Together they watched the sun setting across the water. "Every sunset on the lake seems more glorious," Sam's mother said. "I wish your father could be here to enjoy these beautiful evenings."

Sam did not reply. He was looking out across the water. The sun had slipped behind the western brim of the lake, leaving a whole paintbox of color behind. Between softly tinted clouds were blue-green pools. The colors deepened and darkened. A single star twinkled. Silence covered the water and the earth. Everything seemed to wait motionless, breathless.

Then Sam heard his mother saying softly, "This is the Lord's doing; it is marvelous in our eyes." *

* Psalm 118:23

Deep down inside, Sam felt a quietness so good that he wanted to keep the moment forever. Even when Davey came back and squeezed in between them, neither Sam nor his mother spoke. For once Davey was quiet, too.

Then finally Davey looked up and with a voice full of wonder asked, "Mama, is this God?"

"Yes, Davey," she answered softly, "he's here with us. I feel it, too."

Still Sam said nothing. He could not put into words how complete and perfect this evening was. At least for now the emptiness he had sometimes felt during the long weeks at the lake was gone.

never alone

"Jackie's here!" Pat said as she pointed to a red raincoat with JACKIE printed in big white letters across the back. "And that's Marg's green overnight bag. This must be the right tent."

Pat's father set two suitcases down on the wood floor of the big tent. Pat tossed her bedroll onto one of the cots. Then she threw her arms around her father's neck and kissed him hard.

"The girls must be down by the lake," she said. "Bye, Daddy. I'll see you in two weeks."

"Good-by," her father said. "Don't get lonesome for me."

Pat laughed as she ran down the hill toward the lake. Her father was always teasing. At the bottom of the hill she turned and waved. Her father waved back, and then started toward the car.

Three more campers had come to the cabin when Pat, Marg, and Jackie came back from the lake. Everyone tried to introduce everyone else. For a minute Pat thought she would never get all of the names straight. But by the time the clothes were hung on nails, the bedding and mosquito netting put in place on the cots, and convenient places found for everyone's camping gear, she felt as if she had known the three new girls as long as she had known Marg and Jackie.

When the five o'clock supper bell rang, the work in the tent was done, and the six campers were ready to eat.

"What do you bet I'll be the first runner for our table?" Pat asked. "I always get picked for things like that."

In the big lodge, the six girls shared a table with six other girls. And sure enough, in the count-off to choose a runner, Pat was "it." She trotted back and forth carrying plates of bread, pitchers of milk, and towering piles of ginger cake.

"Did you ever have so much fun, or hear so much

noise?" she asked Marg as the sixty campers scraped and stacked their dishes. Marg nodded her head in agreement.

When the dishes were finished, the lodge grew quiet while the head counselor went over the camp rules and the daily schedule. Then the noise began again. There were songs and jokes and stories before the girls went down to the lake and sat around the campfire.

Pat felt the jolliness fading a little, though, when the fire burned low. A cool breeze blew off the water, and the singing became soft and slow. Suddenly she shivered, not with cold, but with an inside feeling of strangeness and aloneness. She huddled closer to Jackie.

It's the street lights, and the lamps in windows, and the sound of cars that I miss, she decided. Beyond the light of the campfire it's terribly black.

The night seemed blacker than ever when the girls stumbled up the path toward the tent.

"This flashlight is about as much use as a firefly," she muttered to Jackie.

No one talked much. Getting ready for bed it was so quiet that all the sounds of the forest came right into the tent.

Once in her cot, Pat lay absolutely still for a long time, just listening. She wondered if Jackie and Marg and the others were only pretending to sleep, too.

The forest sounded wide awake. There was rustling and crackling among the leaves and sticks, and scampering and swishing in the trees overhead. Something brushed against the tent flap, and a quick flurry of rain swept across the canvas.

When an owl screeched close by, Pat popped her head under the blankets. Suddenly she wished for her own bed in her own safe room at home.

"Am I going to lie awake like this for twelve whole nights?" she asked herself.

Suddenly Pat knew that she had been hearing another sound—a slight crackle in her pajama pocket. She reached in and found a neatly folded paper. Cautiously she took it out and felt for the flashlight under the pillow. Holding both the note and the flashlight beneath the blanket, she read,

"Still awake, Pat darling? Keep thinking about this, and you will soon sleep—

'In peace I will both lie down and sleep;
for thou alone, O Lord, makest me dwell
in safety.' *

Loads of love,
Mother."

Pat darling! Those two words made her gulp.

For a long moment she held the beam of her flashlight on the note. When she turned it off she could see every word—

* Psalm 4:8

"In peace I will both lie down and sleep;
for thou alone, O Lord, makest me dwell
in safety."

"Keep thinking it," she told herself. She moved the blanket down under her chin and settled her head comfortably on the pillow. Lie down and sleep —in peace and safety—O Lord. The words began to blur together as sounds of the forest moved farther and farther away. A friendly, comfortable blackness was settling down so heavily that she could not move.

Just before she slept, Pat's mouth relaxed into the tiniest, drowsiest smile.

"I guess I'm praying," she thought. "I never did it this way before."

the answer

"There!" said Mrs. Ames as she unplugged the iron and put the last of Peggy's blouses on a hanger. With much satisfaction, she looked at the empty clothes basket and went into the kitchen to start breakfast.

"Do I have a clean blouse?" Peggy called from her bedroom.

"Yes, ma'am!" Mother answered. "Come and get it."

"All these!" Peggy exclaimed. "Did you iron all night?"

"Not quite—just since four this morning," Mrs. Ames said. "I woke up before dawn and couldn't get back to sleep," she explained to Mr. Ames and Jerry, who were sitting down at the table. "Too much on my mind, I guess."

"You try to do too much," Father told her kindly.

"I love everything I do," Mrs. Ames said, putting a platter of bacon and eggs on the table. "It's just that sometimes everything seems to be a problem. I have to finish this year's program for the Women's Society and bring it to the printer by Monday. And Day Camp begins in four weeks. If the little cousins are here, I'll simply have to get someone else to be head counselor."

"Oh, Mother!" wailed Peggy. "Don't do that! You're the best counselor at camp. We need you!"

"But the twins and Baby Johnnie will need me, too, if Aunt June and Uncle John have to pack up and move that week," Mother said quietly.

"Well, *I* hope they come!" Jerry said.

"They're darlings!" Peggy agreed. "I'll love having them, too. But, oh, Mother! I do hope you can still go to Day Camp!"

"If I can't, I should be finding someone to take my place right now." There was a worried frown on Mrs. Ames' face. Suddenly she laughed. "Anyway, that huge basket of ironing is finished. At four o'clock this morning it was Problem Number One. I was lying there worrying about it, and suddenly it was exactly as if someone said, 'Get up and do that ironing!' No voice, you understand; just an order I understood without hearing any words."

"And now it's all done," Mr. Ames said patting her hand, "and you have the whole morning to work on your program. Maybe you'll get that problem whipped today, too!"

No one was coming home for lunch at noon, so Mrs. Ames worked on the program right through lunchtime. It was almost two o'clock when she put the papers in the desk drawer.

"Two more telephone calls, and it will be finished!" she said to herself as she fixed a sandwich and drank a glass of milk.

Lying down to rest after her lunch, she thought happily about the finished ironing and the program that was almost ready for the printer.

If only John and June's move and Day Camp could be straightened out as easily! she thought. Quiet little prayers began to run through her mind.

God, don't let June worry about the babies. We'll all love taking care of them for her. Help me to trust you, too. I'm a bit of a worrier. Like the ironing this morning. Was it you who made me think of getting up and doing it right then? If it was, thank you, God. Finishing the ironing started the day off just right. But what shall I do about Day Camp, God? No one will want to be head counselor at the last moment.

"And you'll never guess what happened then!" Mrs. Ames told the family that evening.

"You went to sleep," Jerry guessed.

"Afterward, yes," his mother said. "But right then I just *knew* that Day Camp was no longer a problem. I realized that I had done everything I could do right now, and that I didn't even have to *think* about it any more. You can't imagine what a wonderful, peaceful feeling came over me. It was as if a huge load had been lifted off."

"You mean maybe Johnnie and the twins won't be coming? Maybe Aunt June and Uncle John won't be moving away?" Peggy asked.

Mother shook her head. "I don't know any more about that than I knew this morning. But I do know that whatever happens, everything will work out all right—including Day Camp."

Peggy looked puzzled. "But how could you *know* that?" she asked.

"The answer came from outside of me. It was one of the times in my life when God spoke to me, I think. No words, you understand, but just being *sure* of something."

"Mother was praying," Daddy said quietly. "She was letting God help her think. She was quiet and ready to listen and God answered her. That's how he has always spoken to people who would listen."

# of puppets and people

"What is it—just a piece of fur without a head, or feet, or tail, or anything?" Sue asked. She was looking at a strange object that her brother Jack had brought home from the pasture in a tin pail.

"He has all those things," Jack laughed, "but he's frightened and he thinks he's hiding." He poked the tight little ball of fur with a friendly finger.

In a flash the ball uncurled into an angry, hissing mite of baby woodchuck. Tiny sharp teeth clacked together furiously.

"Now, now!" Sue tried to stroke the soft little back, but hurriedly drew back her fingers. "Watch your temper, my small furry friend!"

"Warm some milk and try feeding him with a medicine dropper," Mother suggested. "And put on heavy gloves to handle him!"

After many tries, Jack managed to squeeze a few drops of milk between the angry little teeth. Soon the little animal quit fighting and grunted contentedly as warm milk trickled down his throat.

Weeks went by. The woodchuck grew and grew. The Ellis family named him Tobey, and they all agreed that he was more fun than any pet they had ever owned.

Tobey ran with a funny, pouring movement, as if his skin were too big for what was inside. When he was listening to something, he sat up on his hind feet, using his ridiculous little brush tail for a prop. He grew tame as a puppy, welcoming members of the family with loving little chuckles.

Jack and Sue loved him and took him everywhere. In the car, he sat upright on Jack's knees and appeared to watch the scenery. A crowd always gathered at the drugstore when Tobey ate an ice cream cone, holding it daintily in small black claws.

Tobey had the freedom of the house in the daytime, but he usually spent the night in the basement. He never touched anything there, and no one even thought of putting him in a cage. Then one evening Mrs. Ellis sorted the laundry in neat piles on the basement floor. Early next morning when she went down to wash, every piece of clothing was gone!

Could Tobey have something to do with this? she wondered. A little noise made her look at some wide boards Mr. Ellis had set against the wall. Under the boards in the angle of the basement floor and wall was the laundry.

"Jack—Sue!" she called. "Come see what Tobey has done!"

"He must have worked all night," exclaimed Sue when she saw the piles of clothing. "But why did he do it?"

"To make a soft burrow," said Jack, laughing. "He must be practicing up for the time when he has to hibernate."

The rest of the summer Sue and Jack kept a special watch on Tobey. Usually he was near by stuffing himself with clover. He grew so fat that his short legs just barely raised his fat body off the ground. But sometimes they could not find him. Sometimes he disappeared for hours, and twice he was gone over night. Finally in late September he went away and did not come back. Jack and Sue hunted and called, but there was no answering chuckle from Tobey.

"Where can he be?" asked Sue.

"He's gone to sleep in a dark burrow on some nearby hillside," Father said. "Winter is coming, and Tobey is ready for it."

"But why should he want to hibernate?" Sue protested. "He knew we would feed him and take care of him."

"He can't help himself," Jack said. "It's instinct."

"But he's one woodchuck who doesn't need to hibernate," Sue said stubbornly.

Father laughed. "He's hibernating whether he needs to or not! You've seen puppet shows, Sue. The puppeteer pulls the strings and the puppets walk, or dance, or nod their heads. Tobey is the puppet, and Old Mother Nature is the puppeteer. Tobey has to do whatever the season orders—wake up in the spring, find a mate and raise a family, stuff himself with clover in the summer, dig a burrow in the fall, and sleep all winter. He hasn't any choice. All living things except people follow the pattern of nature. Only people can choose what they will do."

"Why people?" Sue asked wonderingly. "Why don't we have to obey nature, too?"

" 'God created man in his own image,'*" Father quoted from the Bible. "God planned for people to be like himself. Since men can think, and plan, and choose like God, they can be his friends. And if they can be his friends, they can know his plans and help with them."

"We don't have to, though," Jack said soberly.

* Genesis 1:27

"We can choose to do wrong. If we were like Tobey, we would have to follow God's plan and always do right."

"Being a person is much harder than being an animal," Sue decided. "Choosing is more trouble than following instinct, but I'd rather be a person."

"You wouldn't like Old Mother Nature telling you what to do and jerking the strings to see that you did it?" Father asked teasingly.

Sue shook her head. "And I'm glad God doesn't want to jerk the strings, either," she said thoughtfully. "The right to choose! So that's what it means to be created in the image of God!"

I Wonder about God and Things That Happen

Why doesn't God prevent terrible accidents?

Is it fair for good people to have trouble?

Can God help in times of danger?

What are death and heaven like?

God's will

It was summer in a year just before scientists had the polio vaccine ready to use.

"Now just move over a little while I wrap these towels around your leg, dear."

Ann obediently moved over, but she did not smile in reply to the nurse's warm glance. Instead, she gave a deep sigh. She knew she was lucky. Polio had paralyzed her right leg, but Doctor Gross said it would be almost as good as new if she did the exercises and all of the things she was supposed to do.

There were a lot of people here who were much worse off than she was. But she did get awfully tired of staying in the hospital day after day. It was hot packs and exercises and exercises and hot packs over and over and over. She sighed again.

"Now let that leg stay bundled up for a little while," said the nurse, smiling. "I'll be back in an hour or so to help you with your exercises. And, dear, don't fret about all this. Remember that illness is God's will."

God's will? Ann thought as the nurse left the room. Could it really be God's will? She had heard the phrase many times since she had been in the hospital, but no one had ever said it to her before.

"Well, if it is God's will, I don't think he is fair," Ann said to herself, almost aloud. "I don't know why he should pick on me."

She remembered the fun she had had the summer before on her grandparents' farm. Her cousins, Jim and Judy, had been there, too. Together they had played with the animals, climbed trees, gone wading in the brook, and done all sorts of wonderful things. They had all planned to be there together again this summer.

Jim and Judy are there now, Ann thought longingly. It just isn't fair. I don't know why I had to get sick. If it really is God's will, I'm not sure I like him.

Just then another nurse brought a glass of milk to

drink, and after that the hospital librarian came around with books. Ann chose a book to read and forgot about her illness being God's will.

But that afternoon when her mother came, she remembered again what the nurse had said. "Is it really true?" she asked her mother. "Is it God's will that I am here in the hospital with polio?"

"I can't really believe that it is," her mother answered. "I don't believe that God wants any of his children to be ill or lose the use of their strong bodies. People keep telling me that illness is God's will, too. I'm sure they must be wrong, even though I can't explain why I think so. Why don't you ask Dr. Gross sometime? Maybe he understands it. I've been meaning to ask him myself.

"Look here. I've brought you a letter from Jim and Judy."

Ann seized the letter eagerly. Little papers spilled out. Jim and Judy had made games and puzzles about things on the farm.

"Look at this jigsaw puzzle," said Ann. "I'll bet it's a pig, because there's so much pink."

Ann and her mother had fun putting the pig together. When she was alone again, Ann worked out the fill-in-the-blank games and made the stand-up animals her cousins had sent. She did not think again about the nurse's remark.

The next evening her mother brought another

letter from Jim and Judy. Ann was anxious to open it, but first she asked, "What is Dr. Gross doing? He's been across the hall for hours."

"There's a baby who is very ill in that room," said her mother. "They don't think he will live. Dr. Gross is doing everything he can, but even doctors don't know as much as they would like to know about curing people."

"Oh, dear," said Ann. "I do hope the baby gets better."

It was after her mother had gone home that Ann heard the baby's father say, "I guess it was God's will for us to lose him."

Dr. Gross made an odd, grunting sound as if he did not agree. But Ann did not hear him say anything. It made her think again of the problem that had troubled her the day before.

When Dr. Gross came to see her the next day, Ann had a question for him. "Was it really God's will for the baby to die last night?" she asked.

Dr. Gross looked sober.

"It doesn't seem so to me, Ann," he said. "If God wants people to be sick and die, then why do I work to make them better and to keep them alive? I should be helping God, not interfering with his plans." The doctor smiled at her. He started to go away, but turned and came back.

"Ann," he said, "no matter what you hear people

say, remember this—God wants us all to be well, and strong, and useful. In my work I help him. Some day someone will find a way to prevent polio. That person will be one of the best helpers God has!"

"But why didn't you tell the baby's father that he was wrong?"

Dr. Gross was silent a moment before he gave his answer.

"I guess some people feel better if they can blame God for illness and death," he said. "But I like to believe that these things are just a part of living and choosing for ourselves where we will go and what we will do. Wouldn't you rather be home or at your grandfather's farm than be shut up in a completely sterile place where no germ could reach you?"

Ann nodded. The hospital was all right. But it certainly wasn't as much fun as being at the farm, or even as being at home.

"Look at these things Jim and Judy have been sending me," she said. "The farm is fun."

"Of course it is!" Dr. Gross said. "And if you can have a busy, useful, interesting life, you're willing to take the chance of getting sick or hurt. And you must be willing to take the responsibility for what happens to you instead of blaming God."

"But the little baby wasn't responsible," Ann said.

"No," Dr. Gross agreed. "Someone exposed him to polio without knowing it or meaning to do it.

Someone else was taking the chances that had to be taken so that he could grow up into a fine boy. He wouldn't have wanted to be shut up in a germ-free place either. Never be afraid of taking chances, Ann, when they are the right chances."

"Like going to the farm?" Ann asked.

Dr. Gross smiled. "That's one of the best kinds of chances," he said. "You keep on improving, and we'll have you out on the farm before you know it."

That afternoon Ann told her mother what Dr. Gross had said.

"I feel much better," she finished, lying back with a big sigh. "I always thought God was kind, and loving like you and Daddy—only more so. And he really is, isn't he?"

God was there

Tad was finishing his lemon pie when a shrill whistle broke the evening quiet outside the open window. He washed the last bite down with half a glass of water and started for the door.

"Not so fast," Mr. Austin said, taking hold of his son's sleeve. "We'd like to know where you're going."

"To the park with Charlie."

"Well, remember it will be dark soon. This isn't summer, even if it has felt that way all day."

Tad nodded and ran out the door.

Mrs. Austin poured more tea over the ice cubes in her glass. "Tomorrow is our day to furnish flowers for the church, you know; and thanks to this warm weather, I've got two wonderful bouquets. I put them in buckets in the basement. In the morning I'll pick the white tulips by the garage."

Her last words were lost in the sudden roar of a plane zooming low over the house. She and her husband jumped up and ran to the door.

As they looked out, they saw that a blanket of darkness was suddenly turning the quiet evening into night. A fierce wind came rushing out of the southwest.

Tad and Charlie were running for home, their bodies bent against the wind.

"Did you see the plane?" they yelled. "It went right over the trees. The airport is on the other side of town. That pilot was too low."

"Probably the storm is giving him trouble," Mr. Austin said. "It must be the six-fifteen flight from the East. I came in on it last week. Remember?"

"The white tulips!" Mrs. Austin exclaimed. "Help me pick them. Hurry!"

Tad and his mother and father rushed to the back yard. But before they could reach the flowers, a torrent of rain drove them back into the house. It was as dark as the middle of the night. Mr. Austin touched the light switch and nothing happened.

"Wires must be down," he said. "Just listen to that!"

The wind roared. Rain beat furiously against the house. Somewhere close by there was a mighty crash.

"A tree must have smashed a house or garage!" Mrs. Austin exclaimed. "Never have I seen such a storm." She lit candles in the dining room.

Tad stared out of the window into the darkness, the wind, and the pouring rain. "I wonder what happened to the plane," he said slowly.

There was no electricity for the television or radio, so he did not find out until morning. Then when he went out on the porch to get the paper, he saw big headlines that read:

PLANE CRASHES IN STORM
Thirteen Dead

Tad sat down in a porch chair and read about it. The plane had been coming in to land when the sky blackened and the furious wind swept out of the southwest. Instructions from the tower at the airport ordered the pilot to pull out of his landing pattern and climb above the storm. But the warning came too late. The great wind caught the plane, whipped it over on its back, and slammed it down into a cornfield. The ten passengers and the crew of three were all dead.

Tad showed the paper to his parents.

"Why do things like that have to happen?" he asked.

"I'm sure I don't know," said Mrs. Austin, pouring cream into her coffee. "It's too bad. Probably the passengers never knew what happened, but it will be hard on their families."

"There are risks in all kinds of travel," Mr. Austin added, then changed the subject. "You should see the white tulips! Every one flattened right down into the mud. It's a good thing you picked the church bouquets before the storm."

"We must take them over and arrange them right away, too," Mrs. Austin said, getting up from the table. "Bring some newspaper to wrap them in, Tad, while I get the car keys."

As they carried the flowers down the hall to the sanctuary, Tad and his mother passed the minister's study. The door was open.

"Good morning, Mr. Gordon," they called.

Mr. Gordon look up and smiled. "It is a good morning, after the storm last night," he said.

"We were talking about the storm, and about the plane accident at breakfast," said Mrs. Austin. "Where was God last night when all that happened?"

"He was right there," the minister said quietly. "He was right there with every person aboard the plane. Today he is with every person who is sad because someone he loved died in that accident."

45

"But why did he let it happen?" Tad asked.

"God has given us a world that is always dependable," Mr. Gordon said thoughtfully. "What happens in nature is always the result of conditions."

"What kind of conditions caused the accident last night?" Tad wanted to know.

Mr. Gordon thought a moment. Then he said, "Yesterday we had a day that was very, very warm for spring. The air that blanketed our city was heated. It expanded and began to rise. Colder, heavier air came rushing in underneath it, forcing it up and up. That was the tremendous wind that struck so suddenly. Our warm air was forced up into the cold air above, and the water vapor it held became too heavy to float as clouds. That was the downpour of rain that followed the wind."

"But why didn't God stop the wind?" Tad asked.

"If God had stopped the wind, then the world would no longer be really dependable, would it?" asked the minister.

"I suppose not," Mrs. Austin said slowly, "but I wish God had not let the plane try to land at just that moment."

"God did not decide the schedule for that plane or who the passengers should be. He did not even design the plane or make it. Those are matters he leaves up to us, and we must accept responsibility for them."

46

"Like the white tulips, maybe," Tad said. "Mother decided not to pick them until today. They were out in the storm, and now they are lying flat in the mud. But it wasn't God's fault that they were ruined."

"That's right," said Mr. Gordon. "But remember that people aren't like flowers. People can choose what they want to do, and God will help them in their planning if they will let him. Of course, even good choices can take us into difficulty, but God is with us always, even when our choices lead us into trouble or accidents or death. That is what matters most—that God is with us."

"Yes, I guess you're right," said Mrs. Austin. "I had never really thought of it that way. Tad, we had better put these flowers into water. If we don't, they won't look any better than the ones that were left out in the storm. And we will be responsible!"

though the earth
should change

"It will be very much like a fire drill," Miss Miller
told the class. "In a fire drill we practice how to leave
the building in case of a fire. In our evacuation drill
we will practice how to leave the city in case of a
bomb warning."

As she told about the coming drill, Miss Miller
passed out the monthly letter to parents whose children attended Greengate School. The letter told
about the drill, too.

"Are there any questions?" asked Miss Miller.

There were many questions, but Herb did not ask any. He was imagining what it would be like to leave the city because of a real bomb warning.

The pupils of Greengate School would be evacuated to Ridgeway, a small town twenty-five miles north of the city. What would happen then? Herb wondered. How long would it be before his parents would come to find him?

"If there are no more questions," Miss Miller said finally, "you may copy this week's spelling words."

Herb pulled out some paper and went to work. But he could not get the idea of the bomb drill out of his mind. He had to admit that he was afraid.

That night Herb's family discussed the evacuation drill. The monthly letter asked parents four questions:

"If an emergency makes it necessary to evacuate school children,

1. Shall your child go with the others to Ridgeway?
2. Or will you come to the school for him?
3. Or shall he be permitted to start home alone?
4. Will you be able to bring your car to the school and help with the evacuation?"

"The answer to all but the first question is 'No,'" Father said. "In an emergency I would probably be too far from the school to help. It would be best for Herb to go with the others to Ridgeway."

"In a real bombing you would stay there until we came for you," Mother added calmly.

"How would you know where to look?" asked Herb, a touch of fear creeping into his mind again. "Or what if—you couldn't come?"

"Ridgeway is a small town. We would just keep looking until we found you," Mother said, smiling at Herb.

"If we could not get there for a long time, Son," Father said quietly, "you would not be alone, you know. God is always with you. He can help you think of the best ways to take care of yourself and to help others."

Father reached for the Bible on the shelf by the window. He seemed to know just what he was looking for, and soon he found it.

"Listen, Herb," he said.

"God is our refuge and strength,
    a very present help in trouble.
Therefore we will not fear though the earth
        should change,
    though the mountains shake in the heart of
        the sea;
though its waters roar and foam,
    though the mountains tremble with its
        tumult." *

Father closed the Bible, with his finger in the place.

* Psalm 46:1-3

"Let's learn those words," he said. "If disaster or emergency ever separates our family, each of us will know that the others are thinking of God as their refuge and strength. Let's begin now."

"God is our refuge and strength,
a very present help in trouble.
Therefore we will not fear . . ."

they said together.

Herb's heart began to beat more quietly.

the best for last

"I don't think I want to go to church today," Kathy said. "It doesn't seem the same—not without Bobby."

"Your father and I are going," her mother said. "I think you'll feel better if you go, too. Bobby would want us to be in church on Sunday, just as we were when he was with us. Bobby liked church."

So Kathy went, but it was hard. Only a few boys and girls were there when Kathy arrived. To keep from talking to them, she slipped into her own classroom. Mrs. Gray was putting up pictures. She handed several to Kathy and gave her thumbtacks.

At first Kathy did not say anything. But the silence seemed so strange that finally she said the only thing she could think of. "Do you know that Bobby died?" she asked.

"Yes, I know," Mrs. Gray said gently. "I came to see you and your parents, but you were at your grandmother's."

For a moment they were both quiet again, thinking about Bobby. Then Mrs. Gray spoke, and her eyes were happy.

"Kathy," she said, "I have been thinking of all the wonderful surprises Bobby must know now. God has planned so many happy experiences for us while we are alive that we all like living. And I think he must have saved some of the best things for the last, don't you?"

A little smile touched Kathy's eyes and mouth. "I never thought of that!" she said. "Yes, I guess God would keep some of the best things for when we die. I'm glad. Bobby liked good surprises."

Kathy and Mrs. Gray smiled at each other. Bobby had always been a happy kind of boy. It was good to think that he was happy now.

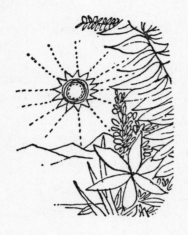

better than we know

John banged the kitchen door, and Mother looked up from the strawberries she was cleaning.

"Well, how was the movie?"

"It was really something." John took a banana from the bowl on the table and perched on the high kitchen stool. "It was exciting—and terrible.

"Mother, was it really like that for the Christians in Rome? Did the emperor let lions kill them, and did people go to watch like we watch a baseball game? Jack said it wasn't really so. He said *Quo*

Vadis was just a story. He said no one would go through all that to be a Christian."

Mother looked over at John. "It really did happen," she said. "Jack is wrong. In those days it took a courageous person to be a follower of Jesus' way."

"That's what the Christians were called," John said, "followers of The Way. They were quiet, good people—not like other Romans with their big houses and slaves and banquets and parades."

"Yes," Mother agreed. "They were so different that the emperor tried to kill them."

"But the emperor couldn't get rid of them," John said triumphantly. "At the end of the movie there were still followers of The Way. And today the world is full of them, and it is safe to be a Christian."

"In most parts of the world, it is safe," Mother agreed. "But even in your short lifetime Christians in some countries have died for their religion."

"You would have to be brave to do that," John said. "I don't know if I could. Jack said that he didn't think he would."

Mother rinsed her hands and began to sugar the strawberries.

"Did you know that the last book in the Bible was written nearly 1900 years ago for Christian people who were suffering the things you saw in the movie?" she asked. "It was written to help them be strong in their faith and brave enough to die for it."

"Really!" John exclaimed in a surprised voice. "I've never paid much attention to the last book. It seemed so strange. Let me look at it." He ran to get his Bible.

Mother and John sat down together at the kitchen table. They opened the Bible to Revelation.

Mother said, "We know this letter was passed about among the Christians secretly. In strange, beautiful word-pictures with hidden meanings it told about the future. It said that proud cities like Rome with their wicked rulers and cruel people would suffer many things and finally be destroyed. This really did happen. For those who were true to Jesus' Way, the letter said, life after death would be filled with joy. No Christian needed to be afraid of dying.

"Here's one word-picture of the heaven Christians would find that comforted and encouraged them in those terrible days.

" 'Therefore are they before the throne of
God,
and serve him day and night within his
temple;
and he who sits upon the throne will
shelter them with his presence.
They shall hunger no more, neither thirst
any more;
the sun shall not strike them, nor any
scorching heat.

For the Lamb in the midst of the throne
will be their shepherd,
and he will guide them to springs of living water;
and God will wipe away every tear from
their eyes.' " *

"Is heaven like that?" John asked wonderingly.

Mother shook her head. "No one knows. People always picture heaven as the best kind of life they can imagine. There are many ideas about it."

"No more tears, and no more suffering," John said thoughtfully. "The Christians in Rome would want heaven to be like that, but I'm not sure what I want heaven to be."

"I don't know either." Mother closed the Bible. "We are sure of God's goodness, though, so we know that what he has planned for us after death will be good." She pushed back her chair. "It's time for me to make the shortcake, John. You can set the table."

John grinned. "I hope there's strawberry short-cake in heaven!"

Mother laughed. "As you grow up you'll discover that even in this life there are some experiences more wonderful than strawberry shortcake. You'll want heaven to be much better than that!"

* Revelation 7:15-17

I Wonder about God and Myself

What must I do to become a Christian?

What does it mean to be a Christian?

a new life for grandmother

"Oh, Grandmother, you're just teasing!" Barbara exclaimed. "You couldn't have been that bad when you were little."

"Oh, yes I was!" her great-grandmother insisted. "It seems to me I was in trouble most of the time. I was a peppery, redheaded, hard-to-live-with little girl."

"What kinds of things did you do?" Barbara asked.

Grandmother laughed. "Well, there was the time I cut off my curls and hid them under the porch because I hated having my hair combed. I didn't look in the mirror when I did it. So when Mother said, 'Mary, *what* have you done to your hair?' I thought she must have found the curls under the porch. I was surprised and a little scared when I saw myself, but I wasn't sorry I had done it."

"When I had those long, thick braids I hated having my hair combed, too," Barbara admitted. "But I would have been afraid to cut it off."

"There were so many things I felt ugly about." Grandmother sighed. "And I'm afraid I usually acted the way I felt. Like the afternoon I refused to wear a dress I hated. Mother put it on me, but she had to jerk my arm to do it. To make her feel sorry I pretended my arm was broken. I held it like this all the rest of that day and evening." Grandmother squeezed her arm up tight against her chest. "I said I couldn't unbend my elbow. Even the next morning I did it. So finally Father hitched up the horses and drove me to the doctor. The doctor just laughed, and when we reached home I got a switching. Oh, dear, I feel sorry for my poor mother."

"So do I," giggled Barbara, "but it's funny, too."

Grandmother smiled. "It does sound funny now," she admitted. "But it wasn't funny then."

"I suppose your parents said, 'What in the world are we going to do with Mary!'" Barbara shook her head and spoke like a very annoyed grownup.

"Yes, they did," Grandmother said laughingly.

Barbara shook her head.

"Grandmother," she said, "I still can't believe you were like that. You aren't now. What made you change? Did you have to grow up first?"

Grandmother stopped rocking and leaned forward a little.

"Barby," she said, "nothing could *make* me change. I had to *want* to. I was just a little older than you are when it happened, and in a way it was growing up."

"What happened?" asked Barbara.

"Every night for several weeks a visiting minister preached at our little church on the hill. Everyone in town went.

"One day my mother said, 'Mary, during these meetings I hope you will go to the altar and let God help you be a different kind of person.'

"That made me think about myself. I really didn't like being the way I was. Sometimes I promised myself to do better, but I never could keep the promise. That day as I thought about what my mother had said, I wondered if God could help me.

"That night, when the minister invited people to come to the front of the church to ask God to forgive them, I went. As I knelt at the altar, I was truly sorry for the way I had felt and the bad things I had done. I asked God to forgive me and help me be different.

62

After that I was *changed*, Barby. I felt sort of new inside. You can't imagine what a good feeling it is until it happens to you."

"Does something like that have to happen to everyone?" Barbara asked slowly.

Grandmother thought a minute.

"Yes, Barby, I rather think it does. You see, all of us are selfish. We think first of what we want for *ourselves*. We know how we want other people to treat *us*, and what *we* prefer to do or not to do. As long as we put a great big *I* at the center of everything, we are not thinking, and feeling, and acting like God's children. We have to let *God* become the center of things.

Barbara's face was very serious.

"I think I know what you mean, Grandmother," she said. "And I hope I can be just like you."

"Then let God be the center, Barby," Grandmother said softly. "You won't be just like me, but you'll be just what God wants Barbara to be!"

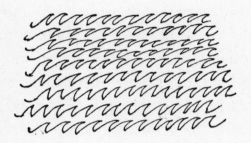

it was worth it

Seventeen-year-old Bill leaned back against the railing of the ship and looked up. Two steel masts rose 100 feet toward the sky. Attached to them were six great white sails.

And to think that I can climb way up to the top, Bill thought. This is the most exciting and interesting thing I've ever done on vacation.

This summer Bill was a helper, a sailor, on a small cruise ship. Different parties chartered the ship for a few days or a few weeks. Bill did whatever he could to help the passengers and the crew.

Five ministers and their wives, and five other men and women had chartered the ship for a short time now. They were on vacation, but they were also telling the story of Jesus wherever they put into port among the islands south of Florida. With them were twelve young people about Bill's age. The whole group was gathering on deck for evening prayers as Bill's gaze wandered from the masts to the deck around him.

Bill liked all of the people on this cruise, and he sometimes joined their meetings when he had time.

"Hi," he called to a couple of the boys. "I'll be over in a minute."

Before he walked over to the gathering crowd, he took one last look toward the sky. Not far behind the ship were towering clouds. A storm was coming.

Suddenly a great rush of wind filled the sails. Bill felt the ship turn onto its side. The railing on which he leaned lay far over. He seized a steel cable fastened to the mast and held on.

Water rushed over the deck and swept people toward the stern. One by one they reached for something and held on. But Bill saw that Mrs. Nelson could not find anything to hold on to. As she washed past he reached out to grab her, but missed. She was seventy years old, and Bill knew she could not swim. There was nothing to do but leap in to help her.

A few seconds later, Bill saw Mrs. Nelson come to the surface quite close to him. He reached out to grab her, and at the same time grabbed a kapok mattress that had been swept from the deck. In a minute they were both holding tight to the mattress.

By now the ship was far off in the distance. Bill knew it would take time before the sails could be lowered and the Diesel engine turned on. As the terrible wind passed, the sea grew quiet again. Black night settled down. Torrents of rain fell.

Minutes went by, then hours, and there was no sight or sound of rescuers. Bill was terribly afraid, but Mrs. Nelson did not seem to be. Cheerfully she thanked God for the mattress.

"I've always liked floating in an inner tube at the beach," she said, "and I'm going to enjoy this mattress just as much. Isn't it fortunate that the water is so warm? And don't you think the rain feels cool and refreshing?"

Later she thought about the people on the ship. "They will be searching for us," she said. "I'm sure they'll be worried and troubled. We must pray that God will give them comfort and strength."

"But what about us?" Bill asked finally. "It looks as if this might be the end for us."

"Yes, son, it does," Mrs. Nelson admitted. "But if I die tonight my heart is at peace."

"I'm not at peace about dying," Bill said slowly.

"I'm a church member, Mrs. Nelson, but now I don't think I know enough about God. Will you pray for me?"

"Of course," Mrs. Nelson said gently.

In the darkness of the night and the sea, supported by the floating mattress, Mrs. Nelson prayed and Bill listened. She recalled promises of God's care from the Bible.

"He's right here with us, Bill," she said happily. "No matter what happens to us tonight, God is with us through it all. Because he is here we don't need to be afraid. Bill, can you remember when you were a little boy and woke up frightened in the night? When your father or mother came and took your hand, you weren't frightened any more, were you? That's how you can feel about God right now."

Waves slapped against the kapok mattress. Bill was silent. His arms rested on the mattress, and his head rested on his arms. He wanted to feel like Mrs. Nelson did, but somehow he just couldn't. He kept remembering all of the things he had done that weren't really right. He wasn't really good enough.

"Bill," Mrs. Nelson said after a while, "is there anything that keeps you from feeling sure of God's love? Are you afraid God doesn't want you because you have done wrong sometimes? Jesus taught us that God is wonderfully loving and forgiving. Just rest yourself on the thought of his love and care. Jesus did that, you know. He said, 'Father, into thy hands I commit my spirit.'* Learn from Jesus, Bill."

Bill listened. He had heard the things Mrs. Nelson was saying before. But they sounded different now. And all at once he understood what the words meant.

"I do believe it!" he said suddenly. "Now I know what Jesus felt when he said, 'Into thy hands I commit my spirit.' It's a feeling of trusting inside that takes away all the fear."

A long time later the hot sun came up over the far rim of the sea. Land was in sight, but very far away. Bill began to swim, pushing the mattress toward shore. The mattress was getting water soaked, however, and both Bill and Mrs. Nelson knew that after a while it would sink.

"I think we will have a better chance if I try to swim to shore for help," Bill said.

Mrs. Nelson looked at the mattress and then off toward land. "You're right," she answered. "And if I'm not here when you get back, you'll know that everything is still all right."

Bill started off toward shore. It was a long pull. But if he didn't make it, it would be all right with him, too.

Then, a few minutes later, as Bill was still pulling comfortably along toward shore, a boat came up beside him.

* Luke 23:46

"There is a lady out there on a mattress," he said. "Get her first."

"I'm here," said a voice. It was Mrs. Nelson. "They came right after you left."

Bill and Mrs. Nelson were both tired and sunburned, but they were safe after seventeen hours in the water.

Never had the port of Miragoane seen such rejoicing as when Mrs. Nelson and Bill stood safely on the deck of their ship among their friends! Even the Haitian folk on the dock shouted and sang.

Someone said to Bill, "What an awful experience —seventeen hours in the sea!"

Bill thought of the moment when he had begun to know God as Jesus knew him, when he had felt certain that he was forgiven, and loved, and safe with God no matter what happened.

"It was worth it," he said. "It was the best thing that ever happened to me."

a new leader

Greg put the receiver down with a BANG!

"Mrs. Matthews again?" asked Father, looking up from his bacon and eggs.

"She says her paper isn't there!" Greg exploded. "I know I left it. That's the third time this week."

"Maybe someone passing by picks it up," Father suggested.

"That's what I think, but not Mrs. Matthews. 'I watch,' she says, 'and you just don't leave my paper.' Why wouldn't I leave her paper? Well, let her go without one. Let her get the news on television. I won't even call the office and ask them to send one out—not when she's so nasty about it. She just doesn't belong to the human race."

"Hold up, Greg!" Father said mildly. "That's one family we all belong to."

"Oh, well." Greg picked up the telephone and dialed the newspaper office. "When the paper gets here I'll carry it to her myself. I'll ring her bell and put it right into her hand. I'll say, 'Mrs. Matthews, please watch tomorrow morning. If I skip you, be sure to call me. I wouldn't want to pass *you* up. After all, *you're* a member of the family.'"

"Easy does it, Greg." Father laughed. "But if you really meant that, you'd be on the right track."

Greg delivered the paper, but he couldn't forget about it. He was still angry when he went to church membership class that afternoon.

"I ask you," he said after he had told the class the whole story, "how can you treat a person like that as if she were a member of God's family?"

"I'd refuse to carry papers to her," said Charlie. "She just isn't fair."

"Wait a minute," said Doctor Gilbert, the minister. "What good would that do?"

"It would make me feel good," said Greg. "She may be a member of the human family, but she doesn't deserve to be."

"What did Jesus say about that?" asked Doctor Gilbert.

"Well," Greg answered, "he taught us that God is the Father of all men, good and bad, and all men are brothers."

"Even you and Mrs. Matthews?" Doctor Gilbert asked, smiling.

"I suppose so," Greg said hesitatingly. "But how can you be a brother to someone like that? She doesn't want you to be decent to her. It would take away her chance to find fault, and believe me, she loves to do that!"

"Then she not only doesn't behave like a child of God herself, but she keeps you from acting like one, too," Doctor Gilbert said. "Is that what you mean, Greg?"

"I guess that's about it," Greg admitted. "But it's hard to be any different."

"Of course it is," agreed Doctor Gilbert. "That's where Jesus comes into the picture. He not only taught that everyone is a member of God's family, but he showed us how to live in the family like a child of God. If we take him as our Leader, we try to find his kind of fellowship with God. Once we are real friends with God, we honestly try to live with other people as Jesus did. He helps put feelings of love and kindness and good will in place of anger and hate and meanness."

There was silence in the class for a moment. Then Greg said solemnly, "I never thought of it that way, Doctor Gilbert."

"Well then, is the Christian life for you, Greg? Are you going to let Jesus lead you into a spirit of love and deeds of service to God's other children?"

Greg thought for a minute before he said, "I'll try, sir."

"Maybe Mrs. Matthews is your first job in following your new Leader," Doctor Gilbert suggested.

Greg's eyes danced with fun.

"That's a big job!" he said. "Do you think I can turn her into one of my nice customers who bakes cookies for me and hands them out on Saturdays when I collect?"

"I'm sure of it, Greg. Every day the loving spirit of Jesus is changing people—even people like Mrs. Matthews."

"And me," Greg said soberly.

a new law for Bob

"This is going to be a bad day," Bob said to himself when he woke up. "Wish I could stay in bed." He couldn't, of course, so he got up, dressed, and went downstairs.

"Wish I could skip school today," he muttered gloomily at the breakfast table. "It was bad enough to miss the Junior Historians' trip. But when I think of hearing all about it today, I feel sicker than I did Thursday. Why should I be home with a sore throat when they're taking a trip on the river, and seeing where white men first settled in this state, and going to church in the first cathedral west of the Alleghenies?"

"Wait a minute," said Dad. "You're only making yourself and everybody else miserable. Try to think about other people. Be glad that the class could go, even when you couldn't. It's the only way to feel happy yourself."

"That's a law of human behavior," Mother added. "To be happy yourself, make others happy."

"Who wants to be happy?" Bob muttered.

Mother and Dad laughed. "Why, *you* do!" they said in a chorus. "Try it. You'll like it."

Bob didn't agree. He dragged himself off to school, expecting the worst.

At school he found a large, handsome scrapbook on his desk. Each page held colored postcard pictures, or sketches, or folders describing places the Junior Historians had visited.

"We did it on the way home in the bus yesterday," Sara told him. "It's all yours."

"Two people fixed each page," Bill said. "Joe and I had the river trip. We got you this little model of a flatboat."

"We decided to let you look over the scrapbook and souvenirs, and then ask questions about anything that especially interests you," Miss Bradley said. "Other people's trips can be boring, and we don't want to bore you. Being sick was bad enough!"

Bob grinned. They were all thinking of him, and it made him feel good. They seemed to feel good about it, too. Maybe it *was* a law—like the law of gravity. Maybe I should try it, he thought. Next time I have a chance, I will.

The chance came when he went home for lunch. As he opened the screen door, he saw his mother at the stove dishing up the soup. On her shoulder she wore a very large and a very strange-looking corsage. Two big faded zinnias had been clumsily tied to the giant leaf of a castor bean plant with one of five-year-old Jeanie's hair ribbons. Jeanie sat at the table looking very proud.

Bob almost laughed before he remembered the law. Then he choked back the laugh and said, "I'll bet you made that corsage all by yourself, Jeanie. It's the biggest one I ever saw. It's supercolossal!"

Jeanie wriggled with delight. Later, she did not interrupt once while Bob told about the scrapbook and the souvenirs.

Works pretty well, Bob thought on the way back to school. I'll have to try it again.

But he found that it was harder to obey the law at track practice after school. He had almost counted on running the 60-yard dash at the meet on Friday. Of course, he knew that the choice would be close because Joe could run just about as fast as he. Just the same, when the coach read Joe's name, Bob ground his teeth together and looked at his feet. He was about to turn and walk away when his gloomy feeling reminded him of breakfast. And breakfast reminded him of the law.

"Think of the other fellow!" he muttered.

He turned to congratulate Joe, and in no time, he felt much better. The law did work! He still felt good all over when he started home.

Supper was ready when Bob arrived. Just as the family sat down to eat, and Bob had started to tell them about his day's experiences, there was a knock at the door. Bob got up to answer and found Mrs. Peterson and Jackie, from next door, standing there.

"Bob," she said, "could you pop Jackie into his bed and stay with him a while? Mr. Peterson is away, and I must take the baby to the doctor. I don't dare take Jackie with me, because he missed his nap."

Bob held the screen door open. "Come on in, Jackie," he said. "I'm the best nursemaid west of the Alleghenies. I practice up on Jeanie."

"You don't know how much I appreciate this," Mrs. Peterson said. "Good-bye, Jackie."

Gleefully Jackie sat down in Jeanie's rocker and began to sing to Jeanie's doll. Bob tweaked his mother's ear as he took his place at the table. "I was going to shoot baskets with Joe and Bill," he said, "but you've got to obey the law."

"What law?" Mother asked absent-mindedly.

"Well, it was your idea—that law of human behavior!" Bob said reproachfully. "I'm surprised at you! Don't you see happiness shining all over me?"

Father grinned.

"What kind of a day did you have, Bob? Not bad, I take it!"

"Nothing like I expected," Bob agreed. "Yes sir, I'm glad I got up this morning!"

to the least of these

The man looked tired and old and shabby sitting there on the curb in front of the church. As families arrived for church school, some of the fathers dropped a coin into the hat he held. He said, "Thank you," in a low voice, without looking up.

Most of the fourth-graders saw him as they came in. They all wanted to talk about him.

"Maybe he is sick," Joan Peters said.

"I guess he doesn't have a job, and probably he is hungry," Sally added. "We should help him."

"Well," said Jimmie cautiously, "maybe we might help him a little. But my father says people like that should learn to work for what they need."

"He can't work if he's sick," Joan objected. "Miss Stevens, let's give him the money in our birthday bank!"

Miss Stevens walked over to the group. "I think your suggestion is fine," she said. "But our class always votes how to use the birthday money."

"Everyone who wants to give our birthday money to the sick man, say yes!" Joan ordered.

Linda had just come in the door. She added her "yes" to the chorus, then asked, "Who's sick?"

"A man sitting on the curb in front of the church," Joan told her. "Didn't you see him?"

"We came in the door from the parking lot," Linda said. "What's the matter with the man?"

"We don't know that he is sick, Linda," Miss Stevens said, holding up her hand for quiet. "But he seems to be someone who needs help, and the boys and girls who saw him want to help him with our birthday money. Let's count it."

The class counted it together. There was one dollar and fourteen cents.

"I want to carry the money," said Joan.

"It was your idea," said Jimmie, "so I guess you should."

The others agreed, and Joan set out with the

money. The rest of the fourth-graders followed.

"We brought you this," Joan said when she reached the man. She put the money into his hat.

The man looked up in surprise as the coins tumbled down.

"Why, thank you," he mumbled. "Thank you very much."

As the children turned to go back, Linda began to whisper to Sally. Once they were back in their room, she said loudly, "Miss Stevens, we shouldn't have given that man our birthday money. My mother asked him to clean up the paper and boxes back of our store, but he said he had to eat first. So my mother gave him some money. He said he would come back after he ate, and he didn't. He didn't keep his word. We shouldn't help people like that."

"That wasn't honest!" George agreed. "Let's go and get our money back."

Jimmie nodded his head. "My father says, 'If anyone will not work, let him not eat.' * It's in the Bible. Sometimes he says that to me."

The class laughed, but Miss Stevens looked troubled.

"Jimmie, go to Mr. Burke's study and ask if he could come to our class for a few minutes. Maybe he can tell us what we should do."

Jimmie was soon back with Mr. Burke.

"What's the trouble here?" he asked.

* 2 Thessalonians 3:10

The children all started talking at once.

"One at a time, one at a time," he said laughingly. So Joan told the whole story.

When she had finished, Mr. Burke rubbed his chin thoughtfully.

"That about not eating if you will not work is what Paul wrote to church people in the city of Thessalonica," he said. "Some members were living off of the work and unselfishness of the others. I don't think Paul was talking about people who were old or sick or homeless. Let's find out what Jesus said about things like this. We can look in Matthew 25:35-40."

Everyone opened his Bible, and the class read the verses together.

"Then the King will say to those at his right hand, 'Come, O blessed of my Father, inherit the kingdom prepared for you from the foundation of the world; for I was hungry and you gave me food, I was thirsty and you gave me drink, I was a stranger and you welcomed me, I was naked and you clothed me, I was sick and you visited me, I was in prison and you came to me.' Then the righteous will answer him, 'Lord, when did we see thee hungry and feed thee, or thirsty and give thee drink? And when did we see thee a stranger and welcome thee, or naked and clothe thee? And when did we see thee sick or in prison and visit thee?' And then the King will answer them, 'Truly, I say to you, as you did it to one of the least of these my brethren, you did it to me.' "

For a minute everyone was quiet. Then George said, "I guess it was all right to help him."

Mr. Burke nodded. "I don't believe Jesus ever waited to find out if someone deserved help before he gave it. If the man is not honest, well—that's sort of up to him and God."

"We did what was right, anyway," cried Sally.

"That's what counts!" Mr. Burke said warmly. "Now I'll go and see what I can do. First I'll invite him to worship with us. Then, if he'll let me, I'll take him to one of the places in our town that can help him. He may need medicine, or a decent place to stay, or someone to believe in him and help him want to work."

"I hope he'll let you help him, Mr. Burke," said Miss Stevens. "And let us know if you hear of someone else who needs help. We like to find good uses for our birthday money."

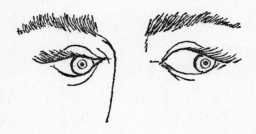

the Golden Rule and cherry pie

"She called the police!" Sam said as he slammed the kitchen door and came in.

"She did!" Mrs. White exclaimed. "What for?"

"Dad was burning rubbish," Sam said excitedly. "He wanted to clean out the garage so we could move our stuff in."

Mrs. White hurried over to the back window and looked out. Sam and Terry joined her. Sure enough, there was the squad car in the alley. "There must be some kind of a law about burning trash in the alley,"

Mrs. White said. "But Mrs. Engel could have told us instead of calling the police."

Sam set his mouth in a straight, unfriendly line like Mrs. Engel's. "I don't want you washing your car in the drive!" he mimicked. "The water runs down against the foundation of my house. The people who lived here before did that just to annoy me."

Terry joined him in quoting the old lady next door. "And those Taylors gave horrible, noisy parties that lasted until after midnight. Sometimes I had to call the police.

"White stuff from your cottonwood tree floats around the neighborhood half the summer. It clogs up my screens and settles all over my lawn."

"Children! Children!" Mother said, but there was amusement in her voice. Sam knew that she thought Mrs. Engel was going to be a terrible neighbor.

"Forty or fifty thousand houses in this city—and we have to buy the one next door to her!" Sam snorted.

Just then Mr. White came in with a sheepish smile on his face.

"Seems you're not supposed to burn rubbish between nine and six," he reported. "But the police were very nice. They said Mrs. Engel calls them a couple of times a month."

"Oh, no!" cried Mrs. White. With a look of comical dismay she sat down on the kitchen stool.

"There's only one way to get along with her," Mr. White said. "We must keep off her property and behave ourselves. And you two see that you do it." He looked meaningfully at Sam and Terry.

"But, Dad!" they said in a chorus.

"You heard me!" he said firmly. "And never talk back to her."

Sam and Terry didn't, but it wasn't easy.

"You two keep out of my dwarf cherry tree," she called to them one day when they were sitting on their own back steps minding their own business. "Just break down one branch, and you'll be in trouble."

"Is your mother in there washing dishes while a great big girl like you does nothing?" she asked Terry one evening.

"When Sam and I do breakfast and lunch dishes, Mom and Dad do dinner dishes," Terry answered quietly.

"Humph!" said Mrs. Engel.

Now and then the police appeared. Boys playing basketball in the alley bounced the ball against Mrs. Engel's garage. Someone parked a car in front of her house over night. Teen-agers from a party rolled garbage can lids down the street.

Sam could not understand why his mother and father were so patient. And he understood much less when he heard his father say to Mrs. Engel, "Yes, roofers are expensive. If you like, Sam and I will clear the leaves out of your porch gutters."

Sam helped with the cleaning, but he resented every minute of it.

"Mrs. Engel likes lemon pie, and she'd never bake one just for herself," Mrs. White said one Sunday noon. With that, she cut a luscious lemon pie and carried the fifth piece across the back yard.

Sam watched it go with a longing look.

He still didn't feel happy about Mrs. Engel when he found himself shoveling her snow one winter morning.

"Maybe we'll be old and crotchety some day!" Father said, grinning as they worked together.

All in all, though they seldom found her pleasant, the family got to know Mrs. Engel very well. They knew just what she did and when. They knew, for example, that every morning at seven the window shades in her living room went up.

But one morning they didn't.

"I'm worried," said Mrs. White at eight-thirty. "I think I'll go over there." She ran across the lawn and rang the front doorbell. Sam and Terry watched. In a few minutes she was back. "Mrs. Engel is ill," she said. "She's been too ill to get to the phone. I called the doctor and her son, and I'm going back to stay until they come. I'll let you know if there's something you can do to help."

Mrs. Engel was sick for weeks. All of the Whites were able to help her in some way while she was in bed. And for once, she really seemed grateful.

After she got better, things began to change. One day she brought over a pie she had baked. Mother persuaded her to stay for supper, and the whole family enjoyed her stories of the city and its people as they had been fifty years before.

Sometimes she called Sam and Terry to come for freshly baked cookies.

Once she showed them pictures of her two sons as little boys.

And once she told them, "You are the nicest children who ever lived in that house. You never set foot in my yard without being invited!"

But still Sam quaked in his shoes the day the baseball went through a window in Mrs. Engel's garage. He and Mr. White had been playing ball in their yard when it happened.

"I'll go get a pane of glass and put it in," Dad said. "You and Terry tell Mrs. Engel what happened."

"But Dad!" they both protested. "Let us get the glass."

"It has to be measured and cut just right," Dad said with a grin. "I'd better do that."

Mrs. Engel had heard breaking glass. She was at her back door when Sam and Terry knocked.

"We were playing catch, and Dad missed one,"

Sam explained, adding honestly, "but I threw it. Dad is getting glass to fix it."

"Humph!" said Mrs. Engel. "Your father like fresh cherry pie? Of course he does. All men do. Fetch a pan and pick some of those cherries."

Carefully Sam and Terry picked the ripe, red fruit from the dwarf cherry tree. Mrs. Engel told them exactly how to do it.

"Now get home and make your father a pie," she ordered Terry. "And you, Sam, pit these cherries ready for the crust!"

"Yes, ma'am," Sam and Terry grinned. "Thanks for the cherries."

"Well, now!" Mother exclaimed. "This is something new. You break her window, and she gives you cherries!"

"I still don't believe it," Sam said.

"A year ago I wouldn't have believed it, either," Mother confessed. "But it never hurts to try."

"Yes, ma'am!" Sam and Terry said, looking up from the cherries and grinning.

Who but the Son of God?

For the love of God is broader
Than the measure of man's mind,
And the heart of the Eternal
Is most wonderfully kind.

—*Frederick W. Faber*

who but the Son of God?

It was a still, starry night in Palestine centuries ago.

Along the Jerusalem road small campfires burned, for many travelers were on their way to worship in the great Temple. Around one campfire men with serious faces listened to the quiet voice of Jesus saying things they did not want to hear.

"We are going up to Jerusalem," the quiet voice said. "The leaders of our people will be gathered there for the Passover, and they will plan together how to get rid of me. They do not know God as I know him. They teach the people to serve him with laws and rules. I ask men to live together with a loving, God-like spirit, to worship God by trying to be like him. So I shall be seized and taken before the chief priests and the scribes. They will condemn me to death, but after three days I shall rise and I shall live again."

"Master!" cried one of the listeners, "Let us turn back! We can go into the hills of the north. There you will be safe."

Jesus shook his head.

"No," he said, "we will go on. It is my work to teach what God is like. I cannot stop because it is dangerous. My enemies will be in Jerusalem, but the Temple will be crowded with worshipers, too. Think how many I can teach there!"

For a time they were all silent. Then Jesus said kindly, "Let us lie down to rest. Morning comes soon, and Jerusalem is still far away."

Next day when the sun grew hot, Jesus and his friends left the road to rest in the shade of over-hanging rocks. Travelers recognized him and gathered around. In the crowd were scribes and Pharisees who gave their time to explaining and obeying the hundreds of rules that made up their religion.

"See," one Pharisee said to another, "he lets sinners crowd around him."

"He even goes to their houses and eats with them!" a scribe added scornfully.

How can I help them know what God is really like? Jesus wondered. How can I help them understand that he loves every single person, even those who do wrong, and rejoices when even one sinner repents?

He looked thoughtfully at the crowd. Around her head each woman wore a narrow band with coins fastened to it. These coins were the savings of the family and were very precious.

"What woman, having ten silver coins, if she loses one coin, does not light a lamp and sweep the house and seek diligently until she finds it?" asked Jesus. "And when she has found it, she calls together her neighbors, saying, 'Rejoice with me, for I have found the coin which I had lost.' " *

The women in the crowd nodded their heads. That is what they would do.

Jesus said quietly, "There is just as much rejoicing in heaven when one sinner learns to do right."

He saw an old man in the crowd of listeners, leaning on a shepherd's staff.

"What man of you, having a hundred sheep, if he has lost one of them, does not leave the ninety-nine in the wilderness, and go after the one which is lost, until he finds it?" Jesus asked. "And when he has found it, he lays it on his shoulders rejoicing. And

* Luke 15:8-9

when he comes home, he calls together his friends and his neighbors, saying to them, 'Rejoice with me, for I have found my sheep which was lost.' " *

The crowd all nodded. They knew how glad any shepherd would be when a lost sheep was found!

"I tell you," said Jesus, "there will be more gladness in heaven over one sinner who repents than over ninety-nine good people who do not need to repent."

The scribes and Pharisees looked at each other in anger, for they were the good people—at least in their own minds. But Jesus was not watching them. He saw how kindly a father in the crowd rested his hand on his son's shoulder, how other fathers smiled at little children sitting comfortably in their mothers' laps. He began another story.

"There was a man who had two sons." **

The clear, quiet voice went on and on telling the beautiful story of a son who was lost to his father and his family because he chose to do wrong, and was welcomed home with great love and rejoicing when he chose to do right again.

When it was ended, faces in the crowd were gentle and kind. Could it be true that God loved each of them, even when they did wrong? Would he forgive them gladly as they forgave their own dear children? They went on to Jerusalem thinking and talking about this wonderful thing Jesus had said.

* Luke 15:3-6
** Luke 15:11

Much happened in Jerusalem before travelers crowded the roads once more, returning to their homes. They had seen Jesus teaching in the Temple. They had seen the angry looks of scribes, and Pharisees, and priests. Some had watched Jesus die on a cross outside the city walls, and heard him ask God to forgive his enemies. It had been said in Jerusalem that Jesus was alive again, that his close friends had seen him and talked with him.

"Some say that he was sent by God," one traveler said to another. "That might well be, for he spoke of God as his Father."

The other nodded. "He died without fear saying, 'Father, into thy hands I commit my spirit!' " *

For a moment the two men were silent. Then one said, "Do you remember the day that he told of the lost coin, and the lost sheep, and the lost son? It was here along this very road. God loves even the sinner, he said, and rejoices when one such man repents."

"I remember," the second traveler answered. As if he were asking the question of himself, he said. "Who but the Son of God could know God so well?"

* Luke 23:46